THE COMPLETE

CαlviN aNd HobbES

Book Two

1987-1989

BILL WATTERSON

Andrews McMeel Publishing, LLC
Kansas City • Sydney • London

Andrews McMeel Publishing, LLC
an Andrews McMeel Universal company
1130 Walnut Street, Kansas City, Missouri 64106

www.andrewsmcmeel.com

12 13 14 15 16 POA 10 9 8 7 6 5 4 3 2 1

ISBN: 978-1-4494-3325-3

The Library of Congress has cataloged the hardcover edition as follows:

Watterson,Bill.
[Calvin and Hobbes. Selections]
The complete Calvin and Hobbes / by Bill Watterson.—1st ed.
p. cm
ISBN 0-7407-4847-5
1. Comic books, strips, etc.   I. Title.

PN6728.C34W38525 2005
741.5'973—dc22

2004062709

Produced by
Lionheart Books Ltd.
3522 Ashford Dunwoody Road NE
Atlanta, Georgia 30319

Designed by Michael Reagan

November 30, December 1, 2, 1987

December 3, 4, 5, 1987

CALVIN and HOBBES by WATTERSON

First there was nothing...

...then there was Calvin!

Calvin, the mighty god, creates the universe with pure will!

From utter nothingness comes swirling form! Life begins where once was void!

But Calvin is no kind and loving god! He's one of the old gods! He demands sacrifice!

Yes, Calvin is a god of the underworld! And the puny inhabitants of earth displease him!

The great Calvin ignores their pleas for mercy and the doomed writhe in agony!

HAVE YOU SEEN HOW ABSORBED CALVIN IS WITH THOSE TINKERTOYS? HE'S CREATING WHOLE WORLDS OVER THERE!

I'LL BET HE GROWS UP TO BE AN ARCHITECT.

December 6, 1987

Panel 1: WHAT'S FOR DINNER, MOM? / TORTELLINI.

Panel 2: OH, NO, NOT TORTELLINI! I *HATE* TORTELLINI!! OH, GROSS! YECCH! TORTELLINI!!

Panel 3: NOTHING IS MORE DISGUSTING THAN TORTELLINI!! CAN'T WE HAVE SOMETHING ELSE? / NO.

Panel 4: TORTELLINI... TORTELLINI... T-O-R...

Panel 1: DID YOU SEE WE HAVE A SUBSTITUTE TEACHER TODAY?

Panel 2: OH, NO! THAT CAN ONLY MEAN OUR *REAL* TEACHER ROCKETED BACK TO SATURN TO REPORT TO HER SUPERIORS!

Panel 3: THEY'RE TRYING TO SUBVERT US LITTLE KIDS WITH SUBLIMINAL MESSAGES IN OUR TEXTBOOKS, TELLING US TO TURN IN OUR PARENTS WHEN THE SATURNIANS ATTACK! EARTH WILL BE RENDERED HELPLESS!

Panel 4: I THINK ONE OF US HAS BEEN EATING TOO MUCH PASTE IN ART CLASS. / I'M TOO SMART FOR 'EM, THOUGH! I DON'T READ MY ASSIGNMENTS!

Panel 1: BEHOLD THE TERRIBLE THUNDER LIZARD, TYRANNOSAURUS REX!

Panel 2: THE FIERCEST DINOSAUR OF ALL, HE IS TWENTY TONS OF BONE-CRUSHING MUSCLE AND RAZOR-SHARP TEETH!

Panel 3: ALWAYS THE VICTOR, HE LETS OUT A TRIUMPHANT ROAR!

Panel 4: LIBRARY / BOOT

DECEMBER 7, 8, 9, 1987

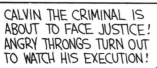
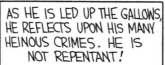

December 10, 11, 12, 1987

Calvin and Hobbes

by WATTERSON

PUTT PUTT PUTT PUTT PUTT PUTT

Z

SCRITCH SCRATCH

ZZ
MMM..

RUB RUB RUB

ZZ
..RRRR..

SHOOF SHOOF SHOOF

ZZ
.OOO..MM..

ITCH ITCH ITCH ITCH

ZZ
YOW WOW
YOW WOW
ZZ..

NKG
K
ZZ..

HMMMMM

ZZZ
Z

THAT SIGH OUGHT TO GET ME OUT OF A FEW YEARS' PURGATORY.

Z

DECEMBER 13, 1987

December 14, 15, 16, 1987

HE SEES YOU WHEN YOU'RE SLEEPING, HE KNOWS WHEN YOU'RE AWAKE ...

HE KNOWS IF YOU'VE BEEN BAD OR GOOD, SO BE GOOD FOR GOODNESS SAKE!

* CLICK *

SANTA CLAUS: KINDLY OLD ELF, OR CIA SPOOK?

THIS SANTA CLAUS STUFF BOTHERS ME.... ESPECIALLY THE JUDGE AND JURY BIT.

WHO APPOINTED SANTA? HOW DO WE KNOW HE'S IMPARTIAL? WHAT CRITERIA DOES HE USE FOR DETERMINING GOOD AND BAD?

AND WHAT ABOUT EXTENUATING CIRCUMSTANCES? KIDS SHOULD HAVE THE BENEFIT OF LEGAL COUNSEL, DON'T YOU THINK?

YOU'RE WORRIED ABOUT THE SALAMANDER INCIDENT, AREN'T YOU?

TEMPORARY INSANITY! THAT'S ALL IT WAS!

THEY SAY SANTA KNOWS IF YOU'VE BEEN GOOD OR BAD, BUT WHAT IF SOMEONE HAD BEEN SORT OF *BOTH*?

I MEAN, SUPPOSE SOME KID *TRIED* TO BE GOOD... AT LEAST, WELL, MOST OF THE TIME... BUT BAD THINGS INEXPLICABLY KEPT HAPPENING?

SUPPOSE SOME KID JUST HAD TERRIBLE LUCK, AND HE GOT BLAMED FOR A LOT OF THINGS HE DID ONLY *SORT* OF ON PURPOSE?

WHO EXACTLY MIGHT WE BE TALKING ABOUT?

THIS IS A PURELY HYPOTHETICAL CASE, MR. SMARTY PANTS.

DECEMBER 17, 18, 19, 1987

13

December 21, 22, 23, 1987

December 24, 25, 26, 1987

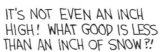

December 28, 29, 30, 1987

December 31, 1987, January 1, 2, 1988

Panel 1: IT'S FREEZING IN THIS HOUSE! SOMEBODY CRANK UP THE THERMOSTAT! WHY DOESN'T SOMEONE MAKE A FIRE?!

Panel 2: IF WE CAN'T AFFORD TO HEAT THIS PLACE, MAYBE DAD SHOULD GET A BETTER JOB! WHY CAN'T WE MOVE TO FLORIDA?!

Panel 3: CALVIN, PIPE DOWN AND PUT ON A SWEATER IF YOU'RE COLD.

Panel 4: AND GO TO ALL THAT TROUBLE?!

Panel 5: I READ THAT THE AVERAGE HOUSEHOLD WATCHES 7½ HOURS OF TV EVERY DAY.

Panel 6: MOM SAYS SHE DOESN'T WATCH TV AT ALL WHILE I'M AT SCHOOL...

Panel 7: ...SO IF I GET HOME AT 3:00, I SHOULD BE ABLE TO WATCH IT STRAIGHT TILL 10:30, RIGHT?

Panel 8: WRONG. DO YOU WANT US TO BE SUB-AVERAGE?!

Panel 9: MOM, THE WASHER IS DONE. OK.

Panel 10: AREN'T YOU GOING TO PUT THE WASH IN THE DRYER? IN A MINUTE.

Panel 11: YOU MEAN YOU'RE JUST GOING TO LET IT SIT IN THE WASHING MACHINE?!? CALVIN, CAN'T YOU SEE I'M BUSY RIGHT NOW??

Panel 12: SHE SAYS SHE'S BUSY. I HOPE THE NEXT TIME SHE TAKES A BATH THERE AREN'T ANY TOWELS.

January 10, 1988

JANUARY 11, 12, 13, 1988

JANUARY 14, 15, 16, 1988

JANUARY 18, 19, 20, 1988

26

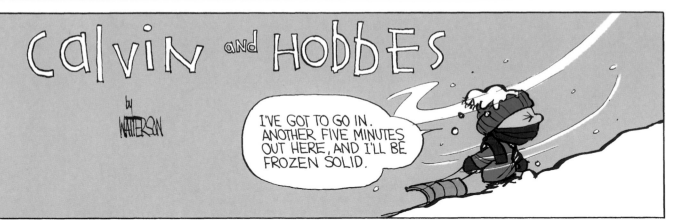

January 17, 1988

January 24, 1988

BOY, YOU SHOULD'VE SEEN THE SPARKS FLY WHEN I GAVE MY HALF OF THE REPORT.

I'VE NEVER SEEN SUSIE SO MAD. SHE ACCUSED ME OF NOT DOING ANY RESEARCH AND CLAIMED I MADE UP THE WHOLE THING.

DID YOU?

HECK, NO. I JUST TOOK A FEW CREATIVE LIBERTIES.

AND THEY CALLED YOUR MOM OVER A FEW CREATIVE LIBERTIES?

GEEZ, YOU THINK *SUSIE* WAS MAD...

DON'T YOU HATE IT WHEN YOUR BOOGERS FREEZE?

HERE WE ARE, OVERLOOKING SUICIDE GULCH, ABOUT TO HURL OURSELVES DOWN AT BREAKNECK SPEED IN A SLED THAT HARDLY STEERS!

RISKING LIFE AND LIMB! LOOKING DEATH STRAIGHT IN THE EYE!

"WHY?" YOU ASK! WHY DO WE DO IT??

BECAUSE WE GET PAID, I HOPE.

BECAUSE IT'S THERE!

FEBRUARY 4, 5, 6, 1988

JANUARY 31, 1988

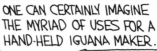

FEBRUARY 11, 12, 13, 1988

FEBRUARY 14, 1988

FEBRUARY 18, 19, 20, 1988

February 21, 1988

FEBRUARY 22, 23, 24, 1988

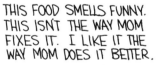

FEBRUARY 25, 26, 27, 1988

FEBRUARY 29, MARCH 1, 2, 1988

February 28, 1988

Hey, Calvin, guess what we're doing in gym today. We're wrestling!

Next period you'll be so covered with mat burns you'll need skin grafts! Ha ha ha! See ya then, twinky.

SIGHHHHH....

PHYSICAL EDUCATION IS WHAT YOU LEARN FROM HAVING YOUR FACE IN SOMEONE'S ARMPIT RIGHT BEFORE LUNCH.

KAPWIINGGG! IT'S CALVIN, THE HUMAN LIGHT PARTICLE!

IN THE BLINK OF AN EYE, HE'S 165,000 MILES AWAY!

NOTHING IN THE UNIVERSE IS FASTER THAN CALVIN!

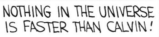

...I HOPE!

MUCH AS I LOVE MY "CHOCOLATE FROSTED CRUNCHY SUGAR BOMBS," THE BEST PART IS AFTER THE CEREAL IS GONE.

THAT'S WHEN YOU EAT THE LEFTOVER MILK THAT'S ALL SLUDGY FROM THE EXTRA SUGAR YOU ADDED.

SOMETIMES I EAT TWO OR THREE BOWLS OF THIS.

I CAN HEAR YOUR HEART RACING FROM HERE.

THEY MAKE THIS CEREAL WITH MARSHMALLOW BITS, TOO, BUT MOM WON'T BUY IT FOR ME.

March 3, 4, 5, 1988

March 6, 1988

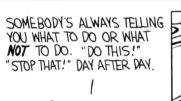

March 10, 11, 12, 1988

March 14, 15, 16, 1988

MY SIDE OF THE WOODS ABOUNDS IN NATURAL SCENIC SPLENDOR.

YOUR SIDE WALLOWS IN DECAY AND FILTH. MY TERRITORY IS INFINITELY SUPERIOR TO YOURS.

YOUR SIDE IS SMALLER.

HEY!

I'M HUNGRY.

WELL, YOU CAN'T CATCH ANYTHING IN **MY** TERRITORY. THAT'S WHAT THE BOOK SAYS.

WHAT DO TIGERS EAT IN THE WILD ANYWAY?

THEY CATCH BIG GROSS CATERPILLARS LIKE THAT ONE.

EWWW. IT'S GOT LITTLE SPIKES ALL OVER HIM. TIGERS REALLY EAT THESE?

BY THE TRUCK LOAD. THEY'RE GREAT.

LET ME SEE THE BOOK.

WHO ARE YOU GOING TO BELIEVE, SOME SILLY WRITER OR A REAL TIGER?

SO FAR, I HAVEN'T HAD MUCH FUN AS A TIGER.

I THOUGHT WE'D BE ROMPING AROUND THE WOODS LIKE WE ALWAYS DO, BUT IT TURNS OUT TIGERS DON'T SHARE THEIR TERRITORIES WITH OTHER TIGERS!

SO HERE WE ARE, SITTING ON OPPOSITE SIDES OF A BIG ROCK. WHAT A BLAST.

BEING A TIGER JUST ISN'T ALL IT'S CRACKED UP TO BE.

THAT'S NOT THE HALF OF IT. IT SAYS HERE WE'RE AN ENDANGERED SPECIES!

MARCH 21, 22, 23, 1988

March 24, 25, 26, 1988

54

UH OH, I'LL BET HOBBES IS WAITING TO SPRING ON ME AS SOON AS I OPEN THE FRONT DOOR!

I KNOW! I'LL SNEAK AROUND BACK AND SURPRISE *HIM*!

HEH HEH! THERE HE IS, ALL READY TO POUNCE! WHAT A SUCKER!

I'VE GOT TO START LISTENING TO THOSE QUIET, NAGGING DOUBTS.

MARCH 20, 1988

MARCH 27, 1988

Panel 1: LIGHTNING FLASHES! THUNDER RUMBLES ACROSS THE SKY!

Panel 2: HORRIBLY, CALVIN HAS BEEN SEWN TOGETHER FROM CORPSES! A POWER SURGE FORCES BLOOD TO HIS BRAIN!

Panel 3: HE'S... HE'S *ALIVE!*

Panel 4: WELL, LOOK WHO'S UP AND ABOUT. HELLO, SLEEPYHEAD. ...OGGG...

Panel 5: CALVIN WAKES UP STARING INTO THE EYES OF A BIG FROG.

Panel 6: SEEING CALVIN AWAKE, THE FROG SCRAMBLES DOWN AND FORCES OPEN CALVIN'S MOUTH!

Panel 7: CALVIN TRIES TO FIGHT, BUT THE SLIPPERY AMPHIBIAN INSTANTLY SLIDES IN AND IS SWALLOWED! HOW DISGUSTING!

Panel 8: I DON'T FEEL GOOD. YOU SOUND AWFUL. YOU'VE GOT A FROG IN YOUR THROAT.

Panel 9: CALVIN THE ELEPHANT WANDERS THE AFRICAN PLAIN.

Panel 10: AT FIVE TONS, HE IS THE LARGEST LAND MAMMAL!

Panel 11: HIS DEAFENING CALL SHATTERS THE EARLY-MORNING TRANQUILITY!

Panel 12:

MARCH 28, 29, 30, 1988

MARCH 31, APRIL 1, 2, 1988

April 7, 8, 9, 1988

April 11, 12, 13, 1988

IF YOU WANT TO STAY DAD, YOU'VE GOT TO POLISH YOUR IMAGE.

MY IMAGE.

RIGHT. SEE, NOW EVERYONE THINKS YOU'RE INSENSITIVE TO THE LEGITIMATE NEEDS OF MINORS.

A FEW MAGNANIMOUS GESTURES WHILE IN OFFICE NOW MIGHT BE IN ORDER. IF YOUR MIND'S GONE BLANK, I HAVE SOME SUGGESTIONS.

OH, THE SUSPENSE.

FOR EXAMPLE, YOU MIGHT REPEAL MANDATORY SCHOOL ATTENDANCE. THAT ALONE COULD ROCKET YOU TO VICTORY.

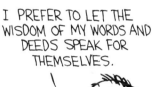

MUCH AS I APPRECIATE YOUR OFFER, I DON'T THINK I NEED AN IMAGE CONSULTANT.

I PREFER TO LET THE WISDOM OF MY WORDS AND DEEDS SPEAK FOR THEMSELVES.

IN THAT CASE, YOU'LL HAVE A LOT OF TIME TO WRITE YOUR MEMOIRS.

WE'LL SEE. NOW IT'S PAST YOUR BEDTIME.

"DAD BURIED IN LANDSLIDE! JUBILANT THRONGS FILL STREETS! STUNNED FATHER INCONSOLABLE— DEMANDS RECOUNT!"

GOOD NIGHT.

EIGHT... NINE... TEN! HERE I COME, READY OR NOT!

ALL RIGHT, GIVE 'EM BACK!

April 17, 1988

APRIL 18, 19, 20, 1988

APRIL 21, 22, 23, 1988

68

April 25, 26, 27, 1988

April 28, 29, 30, 1988

CALVIN AND HOBBES
by WATTERSON

C'MON, HOBBES. LET ME UP INTO THE TREE FORT.

SAY THE PASSWORD.

NO! YOU KNOW IT'S ME! LET ME UP!

YOU MAY BE SOME OTHER KID IN DISGUISE.

IT'S *ME*, CALVIN! LET ME UP, YOU HAIRBALL BARFER!

AN INSULT! WELL, YOU CAN JUST STAY DOWN THERE *FOREVER*, MR. STINKER.

OH, NO! HERE COMES SUSIE! LET ME UP QUICK, SO WE CAN THROW THINGS AT HER! HURRY! LET DOWN THE ROPE!

LA DE DA DUM DOO ♪♫

SHE'S COMING! QUICK! LET DOWN THE ROPE! I'M SORRY I INSULTED YOU! OK? SEE, I SAID I WAS SORRY! CAN'T YOU LET DOWN THE ROPE?!

YOU HAVE TO SAY THE PASSWORD.

..*Verse Seven:* TIGERS ARE PERFECT, THE *E*-PIT-O-ME OF GOOD LOOKS AND GRACE AND QUIET..UH..UM..DIGNITY.

I WAS GOING TO ASK YOU TO COME OVER AND PLAY HOUSE, BUT I THINK YOU'D BE A WEIRD EXAMPLE FOR OUR CHILDREN.

ONE OF THESE DAYS I'M GOING TO MAKE YOU INTO A RUG! YOU HEAR ME?? A RUG!

MAY 1, 1988

MAY 2, 3, 4, 1988

May 5, 6, 7, 1988

MAY 12, 13, 14, 1988

Calvin and Hobbes

by WATTERSON

THE CALL GOES OUT! WE'RE ON THE MOVE!

UP THROUGH THE WINDING MAZE! FASTER! FASTER!

CALVIN SCRAMBLES UP THE GRAINY TUNNEL!

OUT HE POPS INTO THE BLINDING SUN! CALVIN THE ANT RUSHES DOWN THE HILL TO THE BRICK WALK!

OTHER ANTS RUSH AROUND HIM IN THEIR MAD HURRY! CALVIN TRIES TO KEEP UP!

AT LAST HE REACHES THE MONSTROUS DEAD CATERPILLAR! WITHOUT PAUSING, HE HOISTS IT UP!

THE QUEEN DEMANDS HIS TIRELESS TOIL! CALVIN IS BACK OFF TO THE ANT-HILL AS FAST AS HE CAN GO!

WORK, WORK, WORK! THAT'S ALL I'M GOOD FOR AROUND HERE!

I HARDLY THINK PICKING UP YOUR ROOM ONCE IN A WHILE QUALIFIES YOU AS A SLAVE.

May 8, 1988

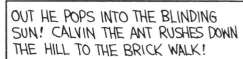

CALVIN and HOBBES
by WATTERSON

THIS IS CALVIN, YOUR CAPTAIN, SPEAKING...

...JUST TO REASSURE YOU THAT, YES, THERE IS SOMEONE UP FRONT.

CALVIN PILOTS THE JET AIRLINER ACROSS THE COUNTRY AT 35,000 FEET.

HE IS GIVEN CLEARANCE TO LAND. BUT WHAT'S THIS? A PLANE FROM A RIVAL AIRLINE IS MAKING FOR THE SAME RUNWAY TO SHAVE PRECIOUS MINUTES OFF ITS SCHEDULE!

IT'S A 600-MPH GAME OF CHICKEN! CALVIN PULLS BACK ON THE THROTTLE AND LURCHES AHEAD!

THE OTHER PILOT TRIES TO CUT CALVIN OFF WITH A SUDDEN DROP IN ALTITUDE!

CALVIN SWITCHES ON THE "FASTEN SEAT BELT" LIGHT IN THE CABIN, AND DOES A BARREL ROLL!

AT 5 Gs, CALVIN HOPES NOT TO BLACK OUT!

AS THEY CLOSE IN ON THE RUNWAY, THE OTHER PILOT HAS NO CHOICE BUT TO PULL UP AND CIRCLE AROUND AGAIN! CALVIN WINS!

HEY, MOM, IS IT TRUE I COULD GET A PILOT'S LICENSE AT AGE 14?

NO.

MAY 15, 1988

MAY 16, 17, 18, 1988

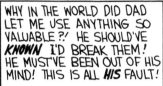

MAY 19, 20, 21, 1988

May 23, 24, 25, 1988

MAY 26, 27, 28, 1988

May 22, 1988

84

CALVIN and HOBBES by WATTERSON

ZZZZZZZZZZZZZZ

FILTH! CONTAMINATION! PESTILENCE! HA HA HA!

OF ALL LIVING CREATURES, FEW ARE MORE REPULSIVE THAN CALVIN THE BUG!

HE EXISTS ONLY TO SUCK BLOOD AND TRANSMIT PARASITIC DISEASE!

SEARCHING FOR SOMEONE TO INFECT, CALVIN FLIES LOW OVER THE PICNIC TABLE!

HIS SENSITIVE ANTENNAE PICK UP THE SCENT OF HUMAN FLESH!

TOUCHING DOWN, CALVIN INSERTS HIS NEEDLELIKE PROBOSCIS INTO A VEIN! PROTOZOANS IN HIS SALIVA QUICKLY INDUCE PLAGUE!

WILL YOU STOP THAT AWFUL SLURPING?! YOU'RE MAKING ME SICK!

MAY 29, 1988

May 30, 31, June 1, 1988

JUNE 2, 3, 4, 1988

CALVIN and HOBBES

by WATTERSON

FWOOOOSH

AS IF LIFE ISN'T SHORT ENOUGH.

JUNE 6, 7, 8, 1988

June 9, 10, 11, 1988

June 12, 1988

June 13, 14, 15, 1988

June 16, 17, 18, 1988

June 23, 24, 25, 1988

June 19, 1988

June 26, 1988

June 30, July 1, 2, 1988

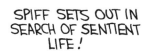

July 3, 1988

July 4, 5, 6, 1988

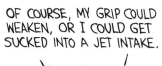

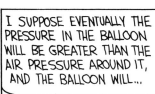

JULY 7, 8, 9, 1988

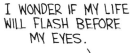

July 11, 12, 13, 1988

I FORGOT ALL ABOUT MY TRANSMOGRIFIER GUN! NOW I HAVE NOTHING TO WORRY ABOUT!

I'LL JUST POINT IT AT MYSELF AND TRANSMOGRIFY! I'M SAFE!

ZAP

WHERE HAVE YOU BEEN?? I'VE BEEN CALLING AND CALLING. YOUR DINNER'S COLD, I'M SURE.

I DRIFTED AWAY ON MY BALLOON AND IT POPPED, BUT FORTUNATELY I HAD MY TRANSMOGRIFIER, SO AFTER I MISTAKENLY TURNED MYSELF INTO A SAFE, I TRANSMOGRIFIED INTO A LIGHT PARTICLE AND ZIPPED BACK HOME INSTANTANEOUSLY!

..."OF COURSE, IF I'D KNOWN WE WERE HAVING **THIS**, I WOULDN'T HAVE HURRIED.

SOMETIME YOU SHOULD TRY TRANSMOGRIFYING YOURSELF INTO SOMEONE WHO OCCASIONALLY MAKES AN OUNCE OF SENSE.

CALVIN, I'D LIKE YOU TO PICK UP ALL THE STICKS AND FALLEN BRANCHES IN THE YARD, SO I CAN MOW IT.

WILL YOU PAY ME?

WELL...OK, I'LL PAY YOU A DOLLAR.

A DOLLAR? I WON'T DO IT FOR LESS THAN TWENTY-FIVE!!

IN A MINUTE YOU'LL DO IT FOR NOTHING, JUST BECAUSE I TOLD YOU TO.

...I'LL TAKE THE DOLLAR.

SMART KID.

July 14, 15, 16, 1988

CALVIN and HOBBES by WATTERSON

I GOT A HIT!

SAFE!

OK, THAT WAS A SINGLE. I HAVE A GHOST RUNNER HERE NOW, SO I CAN BAT AGAIN.

AND MY GHOST RUNNERS WHO *WERE* ON FIRST AND SECOND BASE ARE NOW ON SECOND AND THIRD, RIGHT?

NOPE. THEY'RE BOTH OUT.

OUT?!

MY GHOST OUTFIELDER TAGGED YOUR GHOST GOING TO THIRD, AND THREW TO MY GHOST SECOND BASEMAN. IT WAS A BRILLIANT DOUBLE PLAY.

THAT NEVER HAPPENED!

YOU'VE GOT TWO OUTS.

WELL, MY GHOST ON FIRST JUST STOLE HOME, SO I'VE GOT ANOTHER RUN! HA HA, SMARTY!

YEAH, WELL, ALL MY OUTFIELD GHOSTS JUST RAN IN AND BEAT THE TOBACCO JUICE OUT OF HIM.

HA! THE GHOST UMPIRE JUST SUSPENDED ALL YOUR GHOSTS FOR ETERNITY. THEY'RE OUT OF THE GAME.

HMPH! IF MY GHOSTS DON'T PLAY, *I* DON'T PLAY.

YOU FORFEIT THE GAME THEN! YOU LOSE AUTOMATICALLY IF YOU QUIT!

THE GHOST CROWD SUPPORTS ME. THEY'RE "BOO"-ING YOU!

SOMETIMES I WISH I LIVED IN A NEIGHBORHOOD WITH MORE KIDS.

July 17, 1988

July 18, 19, 20, 1988

July 21, 22, 23, 1988

JULY 25, 26, 27, 1988

July 28, 29, 30, 1988

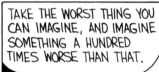

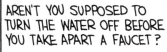

AUGUST 8, 9, 10, 1988

116

AUGUST 11, 12, 13, 1988

AUGUST 14, 1988

August 18, 19, 20, 1988

AUGUST 21, 1988

Strip 1:

"EVERYTHING FLOATS RANDOMLY IN THE ROOM! THERE'S NO GRAVITY!"

"CALVIN PUSHES OFF THE CEILING AT A SHARP ANGLE, AIMING FOR THE HALLWAY!"

"HE GLIDES WITH UNCHECKED MOMENTUM, TURNING HIMSELF TO BE ABLE TO PUSH OFF THE NEXT STATIONARY SURFACE."

"C'MON, YOU! OUTSIDE! YOU'RE REALLY BOUNCING OFF THE WALLS TODAY."

"AW, MOM."

Strip 2:

"EXTRA PANTS..."

"THREE SHIRTS, TWO SWEATERS, TWO SWEATSHIRTS..."

"ANOTHER PAIR OF PANTS..."

"STILL TRYING TO LEARN TO RIDE THAT BICYCLE, EH?"

"I DON'T NEED ANY COMMENTS FROM YOU."

Strip 3:

"A SHADOW FALLS OVER THE LARGE CITY SKYSCRAPERS!"

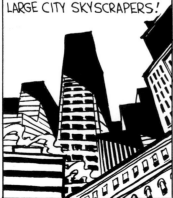

"IT'S A GIGANTIC ANT! WITH ONE FOOTSTEP, IT PULVERIZES THE ENTIRE DOWNTOWN! MILLIONS DIE INSTANTLY!"

"THE ANT BRUSHES THE CITY OFF THE MAP! PEOPLE FLOOD THE STREETS IN PANIC, ONLY TO BE SMASHED IN THE HORRIBLE WRECKAGE!"

"WELL... MAYBE I WON'T..."

August 22, 23, 24, 1988

AUGUST 25, 26, 27, 1988

August 28, 1988

124

AUGUST 29, 30, 31, 1988

September 1, 2, 3, 1988

September 5, 6, 7, 1988

September 11, 1988

HAVE YOU BEEN READING THE PAPERS? GROWN-UPS REALLY HAVE THE WORLD FOULED UP.

ACID RAIN, TOXIC WASTES, HOLES IN THE OZONE, SEWAGE IN THE OCEANS, AND ON AND ON!

THE ONLY BRIGHT SIDE TO ALL THIS IS THAT EVENTUALLY THERE MAY NOT BE A PIECE OF THE PLANET WORTH FIGHTING OVER.

YOU'RE PACKING?

YEP. GET YOUR TOOTHBRUSH, HOBBES. WE'RE OUTTA HERE.

IT'S AN OUTRAGE HOW GROWN-UPS HAVE POLLUTED THE EARTH! I REFUSE TO INHERIT A SPOILED PLANET! I'M LEAVING!

REALLY? WHERE TO??

YOU KNOW, SOMETIMES YOU'RE A REAL LOAD TO HAVE AROUND.

I WAS JUST ASKING!

HOW ABOUT MARS? WE COULD GO THERE TO AVOID EARTH'S POLLUTION.

YEAH! IF WE GO NOW, WE CAN CLAIM IT AND KEEP EVERYONE ELSE OFF IT.

OK, IT'S SETTLED. MARS IT IS.

YOU FINISH PACKING. I'LL GO GET THE WAGON.

WE'RE GOING IN THE WAGON?

OF COURSE! WHAT DID YOU WANT TO DO? FLAP YOUR ARMS?

I GUESS I HADN'T THOUGHT ABOUT THAT PART.

OBVIOUSLY.

September 12, 13, 14, 1988

September 15, 16, 17, 1988

SEPTEMBER 19, 20, 21, 1988

September 22, 23, 24, 1988

September 26, 27, 28, 1988

SEPTEMBER 29, 30, OCTOBER 1, 1988

September 25, 1988

CALVIN and HOBBES

by WATTERSON

UH-OH.

SOMETHING IS VERY WRONG HERE.

CALVIN HAS MYSTERIOUSLY SHRUNK TO A QUARTER OF AN INCH TALL!

HOW CAN HE MAKE HIS PLIGHT KNOWN TO HIS PARENTS WHEN HE'S SMALLER THAN A PENNY?

CALVIN GETS AN IDEA! HE GRABS THE LEG OF OF A PASSING HOUSEFLY AND FLIES TO HIS DAD'S CAMERA!

ONCE THERE, HE CLIMBS UP AND SETS THE SELF-TIMER.

SEL TI

JUMPING ON THE SHUTTER, CALVIN HAS FIFTEEN SHORT SECONDS TO GET IN FRONT OF THE LENS!

WITH LUCK, CALVIN'S DAD WILL HAVE THE FILM DEVELOPED SOON, AND DISCOVER WHAT HAS HAPPENED!

WHAT HAPPENED?! LOOK AT ALL THESE TERRIBLE PICTURES! I DON'T REMEMBER TAKING THESE. WHO'S THAT LITTLE SPECK IN THE DISTANCE ALL THE TIME? YOU HAVEN'T BEEN FOOLING WITH MY CAMERA, HAVE YOU?

ME? HECK, NO. MAYBE YOU SHOULD GET THE CAMERA FIXED.

OCTOBER 2, 1988

October 3, 4, 5, 1988

October 6, 7, 8, 1988

October 10, 11, 12, 1988

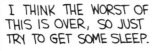

I THINK THE WORST OF THIS IS OVER, SO JUST TRY TO GET SOME SLEEP.

I'M GOING BACK TO BED, BUT GIVE ME A CALL IF YOU FEEL SICK AGAIN, OK? NOW GET SOME REST.

MM HMM.

POOR LITTLE KID.

YECCHHH! THERE IS NOTHING WORSE THAN A SICK ROOM-MATE! FACE *THAT* WAY!

WATTERSON

IT'S SCARY BEING SICK... ESPECIALLY AT NIGHT.

WHAT IF SOMETHING IS *REALLY* WRONG WITH ME, AND I HAVE TO GO TO THE HOSPITAL??

WHAT IF THEY STICK ME FULL OF TUBES AND HOSES? WHAT IF THEY HAVE TO OPERATE? WHAT IF THE OPERATION FAILS? WHAT IF THIS IS MY... MY... LAST NIGHT... *ALIVE* ??

THEN I CAN LOOK FORWARD TO HAVING THE BED TO MYSELF TOMORROW.

FEW THINGS ARE LESS COMFORTING THAN A TIGER WHO'S UP TOO LATE.

WATTERSON

FEELING ANY BETTER THIS MORNING, CALVIN?

NO.

I GUESS I'D BETTER MAKE YOU AN APPOINTMENT WITH THE DOCTOR.

OK.

IT'S SATURDAY, BY THE WAY. YOU WON'T MISS SCHOOL.

I KNOW.

WATTERSON

OCTOBER 13, 14, 15, 1988

October 16, 1988

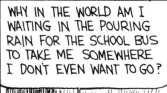

October 20, 21, 22, 1988

148

CaLViN and HobbEs

by WATTERSON

I FEEL A BIG SNEEZE WELLING UP.

...WHICH IS ALWAYS A SURE SIGN THAT I'M NOT CARRYING A HANDKERCHIEF.

AH...AH...AH..

CHOOOOO!

MOM, I SNEEZED AND BLEW MY HEAD OFF!

PULL YOUR SHIRT DOWN, CALVIN. YOU'RE NOT FOOLING ANYONE.

MOM WOULD BE A LOT MORE FUN IF SHE WAS A LITTLE MORE GULLIBLE.

OCTOBER 23, 1988

October 24, 25, 26, 1988

October 30, 1988

OCTOBER 31, NOVEMBER 1, 2, 1988

153

November 3, 4, 5, 1988

November 6, 1988

November 7, 8, 9, 1988

November 10, 11, 12, 1988

November 13, 1988

November 17, 18, 19, 1988

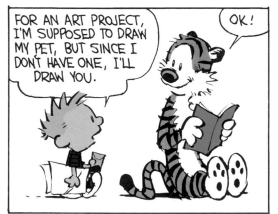

November 20, 1988

WHEN I GROW UP, I WANT TO BE AN INVENTOR. FIRST I WILL INVENT A TIME MACHINE.

THEN I'LL COME BACK TO YESTERDAY

AND TAKE MYSELF TO TOMORROW

AND SKIP THIS DUMB ASSIGNMENT.

MOMMM, I'M HOME FROM SCHOOL! OPEN THE DOOR FOR ME, OK?

WHAT'S THE MATTER? IT WASN'T LOCKED.

SOMETIMES HOBBES IS WAITING TO POUNCE ON ME AS SOON AS I OPEN THE DOOR.

OH FOR HEAVEN'S SAKE! FROM NOW ON, DON'T CALL ME TO COME TO THE DOOR UNLESS IT'S LOCKED.

HA! I SURE OUTSMARTED HOBBES *THIS* TIME!

THBBPTT!

SISSY.

BOY, I'M IN A BAD MOOD TODAY! EVERYONE HAD BETTER STEER CLEAR OF ME!

I HATE *EVERYBODY!* AS FAR AS I'M CONCERNED, EVERYONE ON THE PLANET CAN JUST DROP DEAD. PEOPLE ARE SCUM.

WELL-L-L? DOESN'T ANYONE WANT TO CHEER ME UP?!?

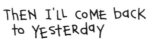

NOVEMBER 21, 22, 23, 1988

Calvin and Hobbes

by WATTERSON

IF *I* WAS IN CHARGE, WE'D NEVER SEE GRASS BETWEEN OCTOBER AND MAY.

ON "THREE," READY? ONE... TWO... THREE!

SNOW!

I SAID SNOW! C'MON! SNOW!

SNOW!

OK THEN, *DON'T* SNOW! SEE WHAT *I* CARE! I *LIKE* THIS WEATHER! LET'S HAVE IT FOREVER!

PLEEAASE SNOW! PLEASE?? JUST A FOOT! OK, EIGHT INCHES! THAT'S ALL! C'MON! SIX INCHES, EVEN! HOW ABOUT JUST SIX??

I'M *WAAIIITING*...

RRRRGGHHH

DO YOU WANT ME TO BECOME AN ATHEIST?

November 27, 1988

WHO MADE THIS MESS OUT HERE?!

IT WASN'T *ME*, MOM! IT WAS...UH.. IT WAS...

IT WAS A HORRIBLE LITTLE VENUSIAN WHO MATERIALIZED IN THE KITCHEN! HE TOOK OUT SOME DIABOLICAL HIGH-FREQUENCY DEVICE, POINTED IT AT VARIOUS OBJECTS, AND...

MOTHERS ARE THE NECESSITY OF INVENTION.

I'M HO-OME!

KAP-OK

WHAT DID YOU DO, STEP ON A LAND MINE?

WHEN'S DAD EVER GOING TO BUILD THAT TIGER PIT I KEEP ASKING HIM ABOUT?

CALVIN, WHERE ARE YOU? GET OUT HERE!

COME ON, CALVIN, I'M GETTING TIRED OF THIS!

I *MEAN* IT, CALVIN! COME OUT AND TAKE YOUR BATH! *NOW!*

SOONER OR LATER SHE'S GOING TO HAVE TO QUESTION WHETHER THIS IS REALLY WORTH THE TROUBLE.

November 28, 29, 30, 1988

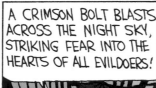

December 4, 1988

December 5, 6, 7, 1988

December 12, 13, 14, 1988

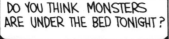

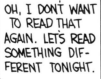

December 19, 20, 21, 1988

December 22, 23, 24, 1988

January 2, 3, 4, 1989

180

January 5, 6, 7, 1989

Calvin and Hobbes

by WATTERSON

"C'MON, WE'D BETTER GO OUTSIDE FOR A WHILE."

"HOW COME?"

"MOM'S GETTING THAT LOOK."

"THIS WILL BE THE BEST SNOW FORT EVER BUILT!"

"OK, THE MAIN FORTRESS WILL BE A WALL FIVE FEET HIGH, AND GO FROM HERE DOWN OVER THAT HILL, WITH TURRETS EVERY 50 FEET."

"OVER HERE WE'LL BUILD AN INNER WALL, IN CASE WE HAVE TO RETREAT, AND A BIN TO HOLD OUR SNOW BALL RESERVES."

"GOT IT."

"HMM... THE SNOW DOESN'T PACK TOO WELL, DOES IT?"

"IT'S NOT WET ENOUGH."

"GOSH, IT'LL TAKE FOREVER JUST TO BUILD THE OUTER WALL... EVEN WITHOUT THE TURRETS."

"I'M COLD."

"ME, TOO. LET'S GO IN."

"MAYBE WE CAN HAVE SOME HOT CHOCOLATE BY A FIRE!"

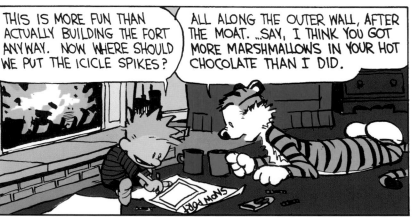

"THIS IS MORE FUN THAN ACTUALLY BUILDING THE FORT ANYWAY. NOW WHERE SHOULD WE PUT THE ICICLE SPIKES?"

"ALL ALONG THE OUTER WALL, AFTER THE MOAT. ...SAY, I THINK YOU GOT MORE MARSHMALLOWS IN YOUR HOT CHOCOLATE THAN I DID."

JANUARY 8, 1989

THE BAY DOORS OPEN AND OUT FALLS CALVIN, THE C-BOMB!

CALVIN IS ABOUT TO UNLEASH THE PURE DESTRUCTIVE FORCE OF A MILLION A-BOMBS!

THE WORLD GASPS IN HORROR AS HE STREAKS TOWARD HIS TARGET!

OH NO YOU DON'T.!!

WILL YOU READ THIS TONIGHT?

"AN ODE TO TIGERS"?

HOBBES WROTE IT.

"THE ZEBRA'S STRIPES ARE LACKING HUES, SO THEY DON'T COMPARE TO YOU-KNOW-WHOSE."

"ORANGE, BLACK AND WHITE IS WHAT TO WEAR! IT'S HAUTE COUTURE FOR THOSE WHO DARE! IT'S CAMOUFLAGE, AND STYLISH, TOO! YES, TIGERS LOOK THE BEST, IT'S TRUE!"

THIS GOES ON?

FOR PAGES. PRETTY TEDIOUS, ISN'T IT?

I'M HO-OME!

KAPOW!

WUMPH!

GREAT. THE SNOW CUSHIONED THE BLOW TO MY SPINE, SO NOW I CAN DIE OF PNEUMONIA.

AWW, HAS OO GOT DE SNIFFOOS?

JANUARY 9, 10, 11, 1989

January 12, 13, 14, 1989

JANUARY 15, 1989

THE FEARLESS SPACEMAN SPIFF FINDS HIMSELF ON THE PLANET CLOSEST TO STAR X-351!

AN ALIEN APPROACHES... BUT IN THE BLINDING LIGHT, OUR HERO CAN HARDLY MAKE IT OUT! IS IT FRIENDLY OR HOSTILE?

WHAT ARE YOU DOING IN BED STILL?! GET READY FOR SCHOOL!

DEFINITELY HOSTILE.

THE SCHOOL BUS WILL BE HERE ANY MINUTE! GO! SCOOT!

SPACEMAN SPIFF, CAPTURED BY VICIOUS ZOGWARGS, IS ABOUT TO BE TRANSPORTED TO THE LABOR CAMP! OUR HERO HATCHES A BOLD PLAN!

AT THE LAST SECOND, SPIFF MAKES HIS BREAK! TAKING ADVANTAGE OF THE PLANET'S WEAKER GRAVITY, OUR HERO IS AWAY LIKE A SHOT.

THERE'S THE BUS... BUT WHY DON'T I SEE CALVIN?

SPIFF ESCAPES!

DID CALVIN GET ON THE BUS?

I DIDN'T SEE. ...WHY?

SOMEONE JUST DARTED BEHIND THAT TREE. SEE, THERE HE GOES AGAIN! ISN'T THAT CALVIN?

THE ZOGWARGS HAVE SPOTTED HIM! OUR HERO INFLATES THE EMERGENCY JET PACK HE KEEPS IN HIS POCKET, AND PREPARES FOR TAKEOFF!

JANUARY 16, 17, 18, 1989

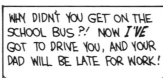

OK, LET'S SEE... IF THE WIND IS BLOWING NORTH-NORTHEAST AT 6 MPH, AND I THROW THE SNOWBALL DUE WEST AT 90 MPH WITH A SLIGHT TOP SPIN....

HA! SUSIE DIDN'T EVEN HEAR ME SNEAK UP!

NOW I'LL CREAM HER CRANIUM WITH A BARRAGE OF SNOWBALLS!

WHIZZZ

PIFF

PIFF

THESE DARN CROSS BREEZES! SHE DIDN'T EVEN NOTICE!

YOU'RE THE WORST SHOT IN THE WORLD, CALVIN! IF IT WASN'T FOR GRAVITY, YOU PROBABLY COULDN'T EVEN HIT THE GROUND!

SMACK!

I DID IT! I DID IT! JUST WHEN IT REALLY COUNTED, I DID IT! HA HA HA! RIGHT IN THE KISSER! HA HA!

BAD NEWS, MOM. I PROMISED MY SOUL TO THE DEVIL THIS AFTERNOON.

OH? THAT RECENTLY?

JANUARY 22, 1989

JANUARY 23, 24, 25, 1989

GET A LOAD OF *THIS* DUMB ASSIGNMENT! I'M SUPPOSED TO WRITE ABOUT AN ADVENTURE I'VE HAD!

I HAVEN'T HAD ANY ADVENTURES! MY LIFE HAS BEEN ONE BIG BORE FROM THE BEGINNING!

HAVE I EVER BEEN ABDUCTED BY PIRATES? HAVE I EVER FACED DOWN A CHARGING RHINO? HAVE I EVER BEEN IN A SHOOT-OUT, OR ON A BOMBING RAID? **NO!** I NEVER GET TO HAVE ADVENTURES!

WHAT ABOUT THE TIME YOU BACKED THE CAR THROUGH THE GARAGE DOOR?

YOU CALL THAT AN ADVENTURE? I DIDN'T EVEN GET ON THE HIGHWAY.

WHEN DO YOU THINK WE'LL GET A THUNDER AND LIGHTNING STORM?

I DON'T KNOW. PROBABLY NOT UNTIL SPRING.

I THINK HE'S GOING TO MELT BEFORE WE CAN BRING HIM TO LIFE.

HEY, SUSIE, STAND ON THIS "X."

WHY?

NO REASON. JUST DO IT. I DARE YOU.

NO.

PLEASE? C'MON!

GET LOST.

THIS MAY NOT WORK OUT AS WELL AS I THOUGHT.

JANUARY 26, 27, 28, 1989

JANUARY 30, 31, FEBRUARY 1, 1989

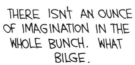

February 2, 3, 4, 1989

CalviN and HOBBES

by WATTERSON

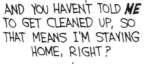

FEBRUARY 9, 10, 11, 1989

February 13, 14, 15, 1989

February 16, 17, 18, 1989

February 12, 1989

HERE WE ARE, POISED ON THE PRECIPICE OF "SUICIDE SLOPE." BELOW US LIE THE SKELETAL REMAINS OF HUNDREDS OF LITTLE SLED RIDERS.

SEARCHING FOR THAT ULTIMATE ADRENALIN RUSH, WE PREPARE TO HURL OURSELVES OVER THE BRINK! WHAT FATE AWAITS US?

READY?

NO.

LIFE AND DEATH HANG IN THE BALANCE! A FRACTION OF A SECOND AND ONE WRONG TURN ARE ALL THAT SEPARATE THEM!

THIS ISN'T HELPING.

DAD SAYS THE ANTICIPATION OF HAVING SOMETHING IS OFTEN MORE FUN THAN ACTUALLY HAVING IT.

I THINK HE'S CRAZY. I HATE WAITING FOR THINGS. I LIKE TO HAVE EVERYTHING IMMEDIATELY.

I CAN'T THINK OF *ANY*THING I'D RATHER ANTICIPATE THAN HAVE RIGHT AWAY. CAN YOU?

DEATH COMES TO MIND.

I DON'T KNOW WHY I BOTHER TRYING TO HAVE A LITTLE DISCUSSION WITH YOU WHEN YOU'RE ALWAYS SO MORBID.

I WISH SNOW WAS DRY, SO THAT YOU DIDN'T GET ALL COLD AND WET WHEN YOU PLAYED IN IT.

...THEN AGAIN, IF SNOW WAS DRY, YOU COULDN'T PACK IT INTO SNOWBALLS. THAT WOULDN'T BE GOOD.

I WISH IT SNOWED IN SUMMER. WOULDN'T THAT BE FUN? ...WELL NO, ACTUALLY THAT WOULD MAKE IT HARD TO RUN WHEN YOU PLAY BASEBALL.

HECK, IT'S OK JUST THE WAY IT IS.

WE'RE GLAD YOU APPROVE.

FEBRUARY 20, 21, 22, 1989

Calvin and Hobbes by Watterson

CLUMP

THE PTERANODON SPREADS HIS GIANT WINGS, AND..

FEBRUARY 27, 28, MARCH 1, 1989

MARCH 2, 3, 4, 1989

MARCH 6, 7, 8, 1989

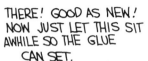

March 16, 17, 18, 1989

March 12, 1989

CALVIN AND HOBBES

by WATTERSON

SIGHHHHHH..

WHAP

SIGHHHHHH..

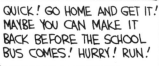

March 23, 24, 25, 1989

MARCH 27, 28, 29, 1989

APRIL 3, 4, 5, 1989

HERE COMES SUSIE, BACK FROM THE PRINCIPAL'S OFFICE. BOY, DOES SHE LOOK PALE. I WONDER WHAT HAPPENED. SHE'S TALKING TO THE TEACHER NOW.

PSST! SUSIE, WHAT DID THEY DO TO YOU? DID YOU GET EXPELLED? YOU DIDN'T SNITCH ON *ME*, DID YOU?

YOU *DID* SNITCH! YOU'RE A *STOOLIE!* A CANARY!

YOU'RE GOING UP THE RIVER, CALVIN.

CALVIN, WILL YOU COME HERE, PLEASE?

SO *FIRST* I GOT IN TROUBLE FOR NOT PAYING ATTENTION IN CLASS AND FOR TURNING IN A LAST-MINUTE INSECT COLLECTION, WHICH I GOT A "D-MINUS-MINUS" ON.

THEN I GOT IN TROUBLE FOR GETTING *SUSIE* IN TROUBLE WHEN I WANTED HER TO HELP ME FUDGE THE PROJECT.

THEN I GOT IN TROUBLE WHEN I TOLD MOM, AND *THEN* I GOT IN TROUBLE *AGAIN* WHEN *SHE* TOLD *DAD!* I'VE BEEN IN HOT WATER EVER SINCE I GOT UP!

WOW. I'LL BET ALL THIS MAKES YOU GET YOUR BOOK REPORT FINISHED RIGHT ON TIME.

MY WHAT?

ONE OF NATURE'S MOST PECULIAR-LOOKING CREATURES, THE GIRAFFE IS UNIQUELY SUITED TO ITS ENVIRONMENT.

HIS TREMENDOUS HEIGHT ENABLES HIM TO MUNCH ON THE SUCCULENT MORSELS MOST DIFFICULT TO REACH.

APRIL 6, 7, 8, 1989

MARCH 26, 1989

calvin and hobbes

by WATTERSON

THREE... TWO... ONE...

LIGHT SPEED!

BLASTING ACROSS THE GALAXY IN HYPER LIGHT DRIVE, IT'S *SPACEMAN SPIFF*, INTERPLANETARY EXPLORER EXTRAORDIN...

SINCE CALVIN SEEMS TO BE ENJOYING THE LESSON, LET'S HAVE HIM DEMONSTRATE THE NEXT PROBLEM.

ZOUNDS! A ZOK DEATH SLOOP APPEARS OUT OF NOWHERE AND FRIES SPIFF'S STABILIZERS!

OUR HERO HURLS OUT OF CONTROL TOWARD HIS IMMINENT DOOM!

$$\begin{array}{r} 11 \\ -\ 3 \\ \hline \end{array}$$

THE SITUATION IS DESPERATE! THIS COULD BE THE END! WHAT CAN OUR HERO DO??

HIS MIND RACING FURIOUSLY, SPIFF SPRINGS INTO ACTION! HE DOWNSHIFTS HIS SPACECRAFT AND...

... STALLS.

RINGG!

OH, DARN, OUT OF TIME.

ONCE AGAIN SPACEMAN SPIFF BEATS ALL ODDS TO SAVE THE DAY!

April 2, 1989

April 9, 1989

I'M HOME!

SLAM!

WHAT A CHUMP!

KNOCK KNOCK

FORGET IT, YOU MORON! I'M NOT OPENING THE DOOR! YOU CAN JUST STAY OUT THERE ALL NIGHT!

OH, I CAN'T *WAIT* TO HEAR *THIS* ONE EXPLAINED.

April 16, 1989

APRIL 17, 18, 19, 1989

228

APRIL 20, 21, 22, 1989

CALVIN and HOBBES

by WATTERSON

I CAN'T SLEEP.

I THINK NIGHTTIME IS DARK SO YOU CAN IMAGINE YOUR FEARS WITH LESS DISTRACTION.

AT NIGHTTIME, THE WORLD ALWAYS SEEMS SO BIG AND SCARY, AND I ALWAYS SEEM SO SMALL.

I WISH I COULD FALL ASLEEP, SO IT WOULD BE MORNING.

SIGHHHHH..

LOOK AT HOBBES. *HE'S* ASLEEP.

HEH HEH... HE SURE LOOKS FUNNY WHEN HE SLEEPS. TIGERS CLOSE THEIR EYES SO TIGHT. I WONDER WHAT HE'S DREAMING ABOUT.

GOOD OL' HOBBES. WHAT A FRIEND.

THINGS ARE NEVER QUITE AS SCARY WHEN YOU'VE GOT A BEST FRIEND.

APRIL 23, 1989

APRIL 24, 25, 26, 1989

APRIL 27, 28, 29, 1989

OH MY GOSH!! SOMEBODY BROKE INTO OUR HOUSE!!

I'LL CALL THE POLICE!

WHERE'S HOBBES?

I CAN'T BELIEVE THIS IS HAPPENING! LOOK AT THIS ROOM!

HOBBES! OH, I KNEW WE SHOULDN'T HAVE LEFT HIM HERE!

MOM, I CAN'T FIND HOBBES! HELP ME FIND HIM! WHAT IF... WHAT IF THEY...

IT'S OK, CALVIN. CALM DOWN. I'M SURE HOBBES IS HERE SOMEWHERE.

I DON'T THINK ANYONE WOULD STEAL A STUFFED TIGER. C'MON, LET'S GO LOOK.

BUT HOBBES IS SO TRUSTING..

SNIFF

THE POLICE SAY THEY'LL SEND SOMEONE OVER. HAVE YOU FIGURED OUT WHAT ALL IS MISSING?

NO, WE'RE LOOKING FOR HOBBES. CALVIN'S ALMOST HYSTERICAL.

I FEEL A LITTLE HYSTERICAL MYSELF.

OOH...I HOPE THE POLICE GET HERE QUICK. I'M SCARED.

THIS IS ONE OF THOSE THINGS YOU ALWAYS FIGURE WILL HAPPEN TO SOMEONE ELSE.

...UNFORTUNATELY, WE'RE ALL "SOMEONE ELSE" TO SOMEONE ELSE.

HOBBES? HOBBES? WHERE ARE YOU??

I TOLD MOM AND DAD WE LEFT HOBBES BEHIND.... I TRIED TO GET THEM TO TURN AROUND AND COME BACK.... AND NOW LOOK, HOBBES WAS ALL ALONE WHEN OUR HOUSE WAS BROKEN INTO!

MOM SAYS HOBBES WOULDN'T HAVE BEEN STOLEN BECAUSE HE'S NOT VALUABLE.

...(SNIFF) WELL, I THINK HE'S VALUABLE.

MAY 1, 2, 3, 1989

233

MAY 4, 5, 6, 1989

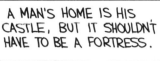

MAY 8, 9, 10, 1989

WELL, AT LEAST WE WEREN'T HOME WHEN OUR HOUSE WAS BROKEN INTO. NO ONE WAS HURT. WE'RE ALL TOGETHER AND OK.

WE LOST A FEW OF OUR NICE THINGS, BUT THINGS DON'T MATTER MUCH REALLY.

IT'S HARD TO BELIEVE HOW OFTEN WE FORGET THAT.

CAN I BE EXCUSED NOW?

YOU DIDN'T FINISH YOUR DINNER.

WELL, I DIDN'T LIKE IT VERY MUCH, AND THERE'S THIS TV SHOW I WANT TO WATCH, SO...

OUR TV WAS STOLEN, REMEMBER?

GOSH, I GUESS I'LL EAT MY ASPARAGUS, DO MY HOMEWORK, AND GO STRAIGHT TO BED, THEN.

AND WE'RE SO PROUD OF HOW YOU HANDLE ADVERSITY.

THIS IS WHERE OUR TELEVISION USED TO BE.

BUT WE DON'T HAVE A TV ANYMORE. NOW WE HAVE A BLANK WALL TO WATCH.

SO HERE I AM, NOT BEING ENTERTAINED.

A POINTLESS EXISTENCE, HUH?

I MEAN, THE WALL IS EVEN PLAIN OLD *WHITE!*

MAY 11, 12, 13, 1989

Calvin and Hobbes

by WATTERSON

TRUE FRIENDS ARE HARD TO COME BY.

I NEED MORE MONEY.

I WISH PEOPLE WERE MORE LIKE ANIMALS.

ANIMALS DON'T TRY TO CHANGE YOU OR MAKE YOU FIT IN. THEY JUST ENJOY THE PLEASURE OF YOUR COMPANY.

ANIMALS AREN'T CONDITIONAL ABOUT FRIENDSHIPS. ANIMALS LIKE YOU JUST THE WAY YOU ARE.

THEY LISTEN TO YOUR PROBLEMS, THEY COMFORT YOU WHEN YOU'RE SAD, AND ALL THEY ASK IN RETURN IS A LITTLE KINDNESS.

WHOOONK!
SOB IT'S SO...SO *TRUE*!
HOOOOT!
THBPBTPTH.

...AND SPEAKING OF "A LITTLE KINDNESS," I'D HAVE A TUNA FISH SANDWICH ANY TIME SOON THAT YOU HAPPEN TO MAKE ONE...

OF COURSE, *SOME* ANIMALS GET ON YOUR NERVES ONCE IN A WHILE.

APRIL 30, 1989

Calvin and Hobbes

by WATTERSON

MILD-MANNERED CALVIN IS STUCK INSIDE DOING MATH PROBLEMS ON A BEAUTIFUL SUNDAY.

NO ONE IS WATCHING! HE DASHES INTO HIS CLOSET! *THIS* IS A JOB FOR...

STUPENDOUS MAN! DEFENDER OF FREEDOM! ADVOCATE OF LIBERTY!

A BRIGHT CRIMSON STREAK BLASTS UP THROUGH THE ATMOSPHERE, AND THEN TURNS BACK TOWARD EARTH!

GAINING STUPENDOUS MOMENTUM, *STUPENDOUS MAN* STRIKES THE GROUND AT AN ACUTE ANGLE WITH STUPENDOUS FORCE!

THE EARTH SLOWLY STOPS ROTATING... AND BEGINS TO TURN IN THE OPPOSITE DIRECTION!

PUSHING WITH ALL HIS MIGHT, *STUPENDOUS MAN* TURNS THE PLANET ALL THE WAY AROUND BACKWARD! THE SUN SETS IN THE EAST AND RISES IN THE WEST! SOON IT'S 10 A.M. THE PREVIOUS DAY!

WHAT ARE YOU DOING OUTSIDE? DID YOU FINISH YOUR HOMEWORK ALREADY?

IT'S SATURDAY! I DON'T NEED TO DO IT UNTIL TOMORROW... *THANKS TO STUPENDOUS MAN!*

MAY 7, 1989

May 14, 1989

239

May 15, 16, 17, 1989

HI, CALVIN! WHAT ARE YOU DOING, MAKING PAPER HATS? CAN I MAKE ONE, TOO?

DON'T BE RIDICULOUS. THIS IS THE OFFICIAL CHAPEAU OF OUR TOP-SECRET CLUB, G.R.O.S.S. — GET RID OF SLIMY GIRLS!

"SLIMY GIRLS"?!

I KNOW THAT'S REDUNDANT, BUT OTHERWISE IT DOESN'T SPELL ANYTHING. NOW GO AWAY.

GIRLS AREN'T SLIMY!

DON'T GET GUNK ON ME. I TOOK A BATH LAST SATURDAY AND I'M ALL CLEAN.

I CAN'T BELIEVE YOU STARTED A SECRET CLUB JUST TO EXCLUDE GIRLS! THERE'S NOTHING WRONG WITH GIRLS!

SEE, HOBBES? GIRLS ARE SO EMOTIONAL.

YOU'RE THE MEANEST, MOST ROTTEN LITTLE KID I KNOW! WELL, FINE! PLAY WITH YOUR STUFFED TIGER! SEE WHAT I CARE! I DON'T WANT TO PLAY WITH A STINKER LIKE YOU ANYWAY!!

WOW, WHAT A GREAT CLUB!

OK, WE'VE GOT A SIGN FOR OUR SECRET CLUB, SO NOW WE NEED TO FIND A SECRET MEETING PLACE.

I KNOW! WE CAN SET UP A CARD TABLE IN THE GARAGE! THAT WOULD BE PERFECT FOR DRAWING UP MAPS AND STUFF!

HMM, THERE'S NOT MUCH ROOM WITH THE CAR HERE. LET'S PUSH IT INTO THE DRIVE.

SHOULDN'T YOU ASK YOUR MOM TO MOVE IT INSTEAD?

NAHH. SHE WON'T CARE IF WE PUSH IT OUT. C'MON.

IN THE PAST, YOU'VE BEEN A REMARKABLY POOR JUDGE OF WHAT YOUR MOM CARES ABOUT.

MAY 18, 19, 20, 1989

MAY 22, 23, 24, 1989

242

MAY 25, 26, 27, 1989

May 29, 30, 31, 1989

244

JUNE 1, 2, 3, 1989

June 5, 6, 7, 1989

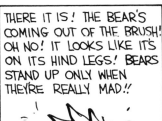

JUNE 8, 9, 10, 1989

CALVIN and HOBBES

by WATTERSON

AHHHH...

UH-OH. SOMETHING IS SERIOUSLY WRONG HERE.

THE LAWS OF PERSPECTIVE HAVE BEEN REPEALED!

OBJECTS NO LONGER DIMINISH IN SIZE WITH DISTANCE!

LINES DO NOT CONVERGE TOWARD ANY POINT ON THE HORIZON!

ALL SPATIAL RELATIONSHIPS ARE LOST! IT'S IMPOSSIBLE TO JUDGE WHERE ANYTHING IS! OH NO!

CALVIN, QUIT RUNNING AROUND AND CRASHING INTO THINGS, OR I'LL SELL YOU TO THE MONKEY HOUSE!

...AND NOW *SHE'S* LOST PERSPECTIVE.

JUNE 4, 1989

249

May 28, 1989

HERE'S THE LATEST POLL OF HOUSEHOLD 6-YEAR-OLDS, DAD.

AN OVERWHELMING MAJORITY EXPRESS AMAZEMENT AT HOW LITTLE YOU'VE ACCOMPLISHED AS DAD SO FAR. THE IMPRESSION IS THAT YOU'RE AVOIDING ALL THE HARD DECISIONS THAT NEED TO BE MADE.

IN FACT, NONE OF THOSE POLLED COULD NAME A SINGLE INSTANCE OF TRUE PATERNAL LEADERSHIP.

HOW ABOUT IF I LEAD YOU UPSTAIRS TO YOUR BED?

HA HA. IF WE CAN BE SERIOUS FOR A MOMENT, I HAVE SOME INNOVATIVE IDEAS ABOUT MY ALLOWANCE.

LOOK AT ALL THESE ANTS.

THEY'RE ALL RUNNING LIKE MAD, WORKING TIRELESSLY ALL DAY, NEVER STOPPING, NEVER RESTING.

AND FOR WHAT? TO BUILD A TINY LITTLE HILL OF SAND THAT COULD BE WIPED OUT AT ANY MOMENT! ALL THEIR WORK COULD BE FOR NOTHING, AND YET THEY KEEP ON BUILDING. THEY NEVER GIVE UP!

I SUPPOSE THERE'S A LESSON IN THAT.

YEAH ... ANTS ARE MORONS. LET'S SEE WHAT'S ON TV.

BOY, WHAT A GROUCH.

JUNE 12, 13, 14, 1989

DO RE MI FA SO LA TI DO

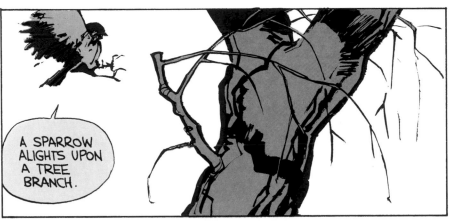

A SPARROW ALIGHTS UPON A TREE BRANCH.

BUT THIS IS NO *ORDINARY* SPARROW! THIS IS A *SONG* SPARROW!

SWAYING GENTLY IN THE BREEZE, HE PREPARES TO BURST FORTH IN RAPTUROUS MELODY!

ON TOP OF SPA-GHETTI

ALL COVERED WITH CHEEEESE, I LOST MY POOR MEEEATBALLL, WHEN...

JUNE 18, 1989

June 19, 20, 21, 1989

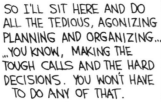

Calvin and Hobbes by WATTERSON

YOU'RE OUT!

DOINK!

I THINK THE BASES ARE TOO DARN FAR APART.

AHH, YOU'RE JUST A BIG SISSY.

JUNE 25, 1989

THE GIANT PTERANODON HOPS TO THE EDGE OF THE CLIFF.

THERE HE SPREADS HIS BAT-LIKE WINGS AND TAKES TO THE AIR! SOARING HIGH OVER THE PREHISTORIC VALLEY, THE PTERANODON IS TRULY A MAJESTIC SIGHT!'

THAT'S IT, THINK MAJESTIC!

I'M THINKING WE SHOULD'VE PICKED A SMALLER CLIFF!'

IT'S TOO DARN HOT OUT HERE.

YOU COULD GO WADING IN THE CREEK.

THIS WATER IS TOO DARN COLD.

YOU COULD GO SIT IN THE SHADE THEN.

THIS SHADE IS TOO DARN DARK.

YOU COULD GO SIT IN YOUR ROOM WITH THE WINDOWS SHUT AND THE FAN AND LIGHTS ON.

THAT'S WHAT I WAS DOING WHEN MOM THREW ME OUT HERE.

I WAS KIDDING.

GIVE ME SOME COOKIES, OR I SOAK YOU WITH THIS WATER BALLOON!

WHY, YOU LITTLE THUG! DON'T YOU THREATEN YOUR MOTHER! AND DON'T EVEN *THINK* ABOUT THROWING THAT IN THE HOUSE!

OUT! OUT!

I'LL BET I'D HAVE GOTTEN SOME COOKIES IF I HAD FILLED THIS WITH *PAINT*.

JUNE 29, 30, JULY 1, 1989

IT'S JULY ALREADY! OH NO! OH NO!

WHAT HAPPENED TO JUNE?! SUMMER VACATION IS SLIPPING THROUGH OUR FINGERS LIKE GRAINS OF SAND!

IT'S GOING TOO FAST! WE'VE GOT TO HOARD OUR FREEDOM AND HAVE MORE FUN! TIME RUSHES ON! HELP! HELP!

I DON'T THINK I WANT TO BE HERE AT THE END OF AUGUST.

AAUGH! IT'S A HALF-HOUR LATER THAN IT WAS HALF AN HOUR AGO! RUN! RUN!

MOM TOOK ME TO THE LIBRARY TODAY, DAD.

THAT'S NICE. DID YOU GET OUT A BOOK?

YEP. IT'S GREAT! I HAD NO IDEA BOOKS COULD BE SO MUCH FUN.

AND YOU'LL LEARN THINGS, TOO.

I'LL SAY! MY BOOK SAYS THAT THIS ONE WASP LAYS ITS EGG ON A SPIDER, SO WHEN THE EGG HATCHES, THE LARVA EATS THE SPIDER, SAVING THE VITAL ORGANS FOR LAST, SO THE SPIDER STAYS ALIVE WHILE IT'S BEING DEVOURED!

GROSS, HUH?

ISN'T THERE A STREET CORNER WHERE HE COULD HANG OUT INSTEAD?

AND COLOR PICTURES, TOO! WANT TO SEE 'EM?

I'M DESTINED FOR GREATNESS, I JUST KNOW IT. "CALVIN THE GREAT," THEY'LL CALL ME.

AND THINK HOW LUCKY *YOU'LL* BE! YOU'LL GET TO TELL EVERYONE HOW YOU KNEW ME AS A KID! WHAT A PRIVILEGE!

IN FACT, ALL THE PAPERS AND MAGAZINES WILL PROBABLY WANT TO INTERVIEW YOU TO FIND OUT WHAT I'M REALLY LIKE.

AND BOY, WILL YOU HAVE TO COUGH UP TO KEEP ME QUIET.

AND WHAT'S *THAT* SUPPOSED TO MEAN?!

July 3, 4, 5, 1989

JULY 6, 7, 8, 1989

263

HMPH.

YES! THE INCREDIBLE SPACEMAN SPIFF SURVIVES! DAZED, BUT UNHURT, OUR HERO CRAWLS FROM THE SMOLDERING WRECKAGE!

SPIFF SETS OFF ACROSS THE PLANET SURFACE. AN OMINOUS, SHADOWY FIGURE FLITS ACROSS A NEARBY HILLTOP! AN ALIEN!

OUR HERO DARTS BEHIND A ROCK AND SETS HIS ZORCHER ON "SHAKE AND BAKE." THE ALIEN APPROACHES!

HI CALVIN! I SEE YOU, SO YOU CAN STOP HIDING NOW! ARE YOU PLAYING COWBOYS OR SOMETHING? CAN I PLAY TOO?

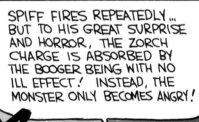

ZOUNDS! THE BOOGER BEING IS IN ALLIANCE WITH THE NAGGON MOTHER SHIP THAT SHOT SPIFF DOWN IN THE FIRST PLACE! OUR HERO OPTS FOR A SPEEDY GETAWAY!

July 9, 1989

JULY 16, 1989

July 20, 21, 22, 1989

JULY 24, 25, 26, 1989

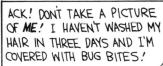

JULY 27, 28, 29, 1989

July 31, August 1, 2, 1989

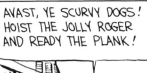

August 6, 1989

I PERFORMED A SCIENTIFIC EXPERIMENT TODAY.

YOU KNOW HOW MAPS ALWAYS SHOW NORTH AS UP AND SOUTH AS DOWN? I WANTED TO SEE IF THAT WAS TRUE OR NOT.

WHAT DID YOU FIND OUT?

NOT MUCH. YOUR COMPASS DIDN'T SURVIVE THE TRIP SOUTH FROM THE TOP OF THE TREE.

MY COMPASS?!

LET ME KNOW WHEN YOU GET A NEW ONE. MY JUNIOR SCIENTIST BOOK SAYS NOT TO GET DISCOURAGED BY TEMPORARY SETBACKS.

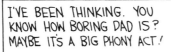

I'VE BEEN THINKING. YOU KNOW HOW BORING DAD IS? MAYBE IT'S A BIG PHONY ACT!

MAYBE AFTER HE PUTS US TO BED, DAD DONS SOME WEIRD COSTUME AND GOES OUT FIGHTING CRIME! MAYBE THIS WHOLE "DAD" STUFF IS JUST A SECRET IDENTITY!

MAYBE THE MAYOR CALLS DAD ON A SECRET HOT LINE WHENEVER THE CITY'S IN TROUBLE! MAYBE DAD'S A MASKED SUPERHERO!

IF THAT'S TRUE HE SHOULD DRIVE A COOLER CAR.

I KNOW. OURS DOESN'T EVEN HAVE A CASSETTE DECK.

THERE'S THE STEGOSAURUS OUT FRONT! THERE'S THE NATURAL HISTORY MUSEUM! HOORAY!

I CAN'T WAIT TO SEE ALL THE DINOSAURS! C'MON, LET'S HURRY!

IT'S CERTAINLY BEEN A WHILE SINCE WE'VE BEEN HERE, HASN'T IT?

AT THE MUSEUM'S REQUEST, YES.

OH, THAT'S RIGHT. CALVIN, NO BITING PEOPLE THIS TIME, REMEMBER?

RROWRR

WHAT KIND OF DINOSAUR DID YOU SAY THIS WAS?

IT'S A STEGOSAURUS!

HE LOOKS PRETTY FEROCIOUS.

NO, HE WAS A PLANT EATER. THE TAIL SPIKES WERE FOR SELF-DEFENSE.

OH. DID TYRANNOSAURS FIGHT THESE?

OF COURSE NOT, MOM! TYRANNOSAURS CAME MILLIONS OF YEARS LATER!

LOOK, TRY NOT TO EMBARRASS ME WHEN WE GO INSIDE, OK?

WHY ARE WE GOING HERE IF HE ALREADY KNOWS EVERY-THING?

LOOK, HOBBES, HERE'S AN ANCESTOR OF *YOURS!* A SABER-TOOTHED TIGER!

HA HA, I'LL BET *HE* WAS POPULAR! IF ANYONE NEEDED TO OPEN A CAN OF JUICE, THEY'D JUST PUT HIM OVER IT AND HIT HIM ON THE HEAD! HA HA!

HEE HEE, I'LL BET THEY DIED OUT BECAUSE THEY COULDN'T UNDERSTAND EACH OTHER! THEY PWOBABBY DOKKED WIKE DIFF! HA HA HA!

...ALL IN ALL, THOUGH, THEY WERE UNDOUBTEDLY THE PINNACLE OF PREHISTORIC EVOLUTION...

LOOK, MOM, THE MUSEUM HAS A GIFT SHOP!

CAN I BUY SOMETHING? THEY'VE GOT DINOSAUR BOOKS, DINOSAUR MODELS, DINOSAUR T-SHIRTS, DINOSAUR POSTERS...

I DON'T THINK YOU NEED ANY MORE DINOSAUR STUFF, CALVIN.

BUT MOM, IT'S ALL *EDUCATIONAL!* YOU WANT ME TO *LEARN,* DON'T YOU??

BOY, SHE FELL FOR *THAT* ONE.

I'LL SAY! I WONDER IF WE COULD GET ANY BATMAN JUNK THIS WAY.

AUGUST 10, 11, 12, 1989

August 14, 15, 16, 1989

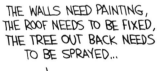

AUGUST 17, 18, 19, 1989

CALVIN and HOBBES by WATTERSON

A 30-TON BRONTOSAURUS

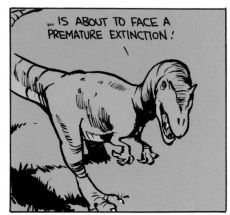

... IS ABOUT TO FACE A PREMATURE EXTINCTION!

THE ALLOSAURUS, FEARSOME PREDATOR OF THE JURASSIC, STALKS HIS PREY!

THE HERD OF BRONTOSAURS IS UNAWARE OF HIS PRESENCE!

SPOTTING A STRAGGLER, THE ALLOSAURUS LUNGES!

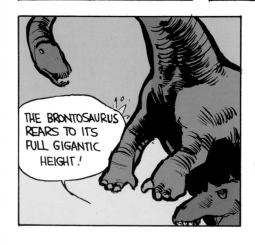

THE BRONTOSAURUS REARS TO ITS FULL GIGANTIC HEIGHT!

WHAT INDUCES AN ALLOSAURUS TO ATTACK A MONSTER MORE THAN TWICE HIS OWN SIZE??

I'M HUNGRY!

THE HAMBURGERS ARE COOKING! NOW GET OFF ME!

AUGUST 20, 1989

CALVIN THE HUMMINGBIRD ZIPS BY WITH A LOUD WHIR!

ALTHOUGH SMALL, HE PUTS OUT TREMENDOUS ENERGY. TO HOVER, HIS WINGS BEAT HUNDREDS OF TIMES EACH SECOND!

WHAT FUELS THIS INCREDIBLE METABOLISM? CONCENTRATED SUGAR WATER! HE DRINKS HALF HIS WEIGHT A DAY!

...PREFERABLY LOADED WITH CAFFEINE.

ARE YOU DRINKING MORE SODA POP?!

SLURRPP

"ONCE UPON A TIME THERE WAS..."

HOLD IT.

WHAT'S THE MATTER?

HAS THIS BOOK BEEN A BEST SELLER? HAS THE AUTHOR WON A PULITZER? DID THE NEW YORK TIMES LIKE IT?

I ONLY WANT STORIES THAT COME HIGHLY RECOMMENDED. ARE THERE ANY LAUDATORY QUOTES ON THE DUST JACKET?

AHEM..."ONCE UPON A TIME THERE WAS A NOISY KID WHO STARTED GOING TO BED WITHOUT A STORY."

HAS THIS BOOK BEEN MADE INTO A MOVIE? COULD WE BE WATCHING THIS ON VIDEO?

WHAT ARE YOU DOING?

I'M PRACTICING MY SNEERS.

THERE'S NOTHING LIKE A GOOD SNEER TO DRY UP CONVERSATION. HOW'S MINE LOOK?

AWFUL!

THANKS. WITH THIS SNEER, I HOPE TO BE AN UNBEARABLE BURDEN AT ANY SOCIAL OCCASION.

THAT WILL GIVE YOU A REAL HEAD START ON BEING A TEEN-AGER.

I KNOW! IT'S LIKE GETTING SEVEN EXTRA YEARS!

AUGUST 21, 22, 23, 1989

AUGUST 24, 25, 26, 1989

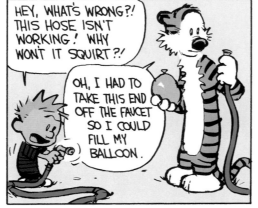

AUGUST 27, 1989

August 28, 29, 30, 1989

296

AUGUST 31, SEPTEMBER 1, 2, 1989

SEPTEMBER 3, 1989

September 4, 5, 6, 1989

THE FEARLESS SPACEMAN SPIFF IS BEING PURSUED ACROSS THE GALAXY BY DREADED SCUM BEINGS!

THEY'RE GAINING! SPIFF'S ONLY CHANCE TO LOSE THEM IS TO RELEASE A GIANT SMOKE CLOUD BEHIND HIS SPACECRAFT! OUR HERO THROWS THE LEVER!

HEH HEH... JUST UH, CLAPPING THE ERASERS, HEH HEH... (COUGH)

YOU AGAIN?

* SIGHHHH * I CAN'T BELIEVE IT'S NOT EVEN 8:30 YET.

WHAT A DAY.

I'M HO-O-AAAH!

KAPOINWW!!

THINGS GET SO DARN QUIET WHEN YOU'RE NOT AROUND.

THERE'S GOING TO BE SOME RUCKUS NOW, BUDDY-BOY!

IS IT? IT IS! IT'S SATURDAY! OH BOY!

NO SCHOOL! NO HOMEWORK! JUST CARTOONS AND FUN THE WHOLE DAY LONG!

HOORAY!

TURN ON THE TV! GET OUT THE CEREAL!

IT'S SAAAAT URDAY!

YOU'RE GETTING UP?? IT'S BARELY LIGHT OUT!

I'M GOING TO THE OFFICE AND GET SOME SLEEP.

SEPTEMBER 7, 8, 9, 1989

September 10, 1989

September 11, 12, 13, 1989

BY GOLLY, I **AM** GOING TO STEAL MY TRUCK BACK FROM MOE! IT'S MINE AND HE HAS NO RIGHT TO HAVE IT!

I'LL JUST SNEAK UP BEHIND THE SWINGS HERE, AND WHEN MOE'S NOT LOOKING, I'LL RUN UP, GRAB THE TRUCK AND TAKE OFF!

THIS PLAYGROUND SHOULD HAVE ONE OF THOSE AUTOMATIC INSURANCE MACHINES LIKE THEY HAVE IN AIRPORTS.

OK, MOE'S GOT HIS BACK TO ME! NOW I'LL ZIP OVER, STEAL MY TRUCK BACK AND RUN LIKE CRAZY!

HE'LL NEVER KNOW WHAT HIT HIM! BY THE TIME HE SEES THE TRUCK IS GONE, I'LL BE A MILE AWAY! IT'S A FAIL-PROOF PLAN! NOTHING CAN GO WRONG! IT'S A SNAP!

THERE'S NO REASON TO HESITATE. IT'LL BE OVER IN A SPLIT SECOND, AND I'LL SURE BE GLAD TO HAVE MY TRUCK BACK! I'LL JUST DO IT AND BE DONE! NOTHING TO IT! IT'S EASY!

OBVIOUSLY MY BODY DOESN'T BELIEVE A WORD MY BRAIN IS SAYING.

PHOOEY, WHO AM I KIDDING? I'D NEVER GET AWAY WITH STEALING MY TRUCK BACK FROM MOE. THE UGLY GALOOT IS THE SIZE OF A BUICK.

HMM... SINCE I CAN'T **FIGHT** HIM, MAYBE I SHOULD TRY **TALKING** TO HIM. MAYBE IF I REASONED WITH HIM, HE'D SEE **MY** SIDE.

MAYBE HE'D REALIZE THAT STEALING HURTS PEOPLE, AND MAYBE HE'D RETURN MY TRUCK **WILLINGLY**.

MAYBE IF I'M REALLY LUCKY I WON'T GO THROUGH LIFE WITH THE NICKNAME "OMELET FACE."

September 14, 15, 16, 1989

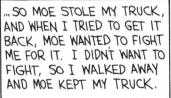

September 18, 19, 20, 1989

September 21, 22, 23, 1989

September 24, 1989

September 25, 26, 27, 1989

SEPTEMBER 28, 29, 30, 1989

OCTOBER 5, 6, 7, 1989

GISZH! ... GISZH! ...

...GISZH!

OH, NO! IT'S THE MIDDLE OF RECESS AND THERE'S A TYRANNOSAURUS ON THE PLAYGROUND!

THE KIDS AT THE TOP OF THE SLIDE ARE THE FIRST TO GO! HOW IRONIC THAT THEY HAD PUSHED AND FOUGHT EACH OTHER TO BE THERE!

PANDEMONIUM ENSUES! TEACHERS LINE THE KIDS UP TO GO INSIDE, BUT THAT PROVES TO BE A SAD MISTAKE!

WALKING QUIETLY IN SINGLE FILE, THE KIDS ARE GOBBLED UP LIKE CHILDREN McNUGGETS!

SOON THE PLAYGROUND IS EMPTY! IT'S ALL HIS! THE TYRANNOSAUR LETS OUT A TRIUMPHANT ROAR!

SAY, WHERE'S CALVIN? RECESS IS OVER. DIDN'T HE SEE US LINE UP TO COME IN?

I SEE HIM, MISS WORMWOOD! HE'S OUT BY THE SWINGS AND HE'S YELLING OR SOMETHING!

October 1, 1989

October 9, 10, 11, 1989

STUPENDOUS MAN CIRCLES THE EARTH WITH A 200-INCH TELESCOPE LENS!

ALIGNED PERFECTLY WITH THE SUN, THE MAGNIFYING LENS FOCUSES THE TERRIBLE SOLAR ENERGY...

...AND FRIES A CERTAIN ELEMENTARY SCHOOL CLEAN OFF THE MAP!

NOW MILD-MANNERED CALVIN HAS NO NEED TO DO HIS HOMEWORK EVER AGAIN! LIBERTY PREVAILS!

HOW'S YOUR HOMEWORK COMING, CALVIN?

UH OH, IT'S MY ARCH-NEMESIS, **MOM-LADY!** SHE CAN'T DISCOVER MY SECRET IDENTITY!

CALVIN? ARE YOU DOING YOUR HOMEWORK IN THERE?

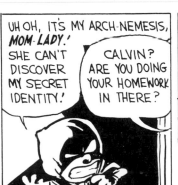

QUICKLY, **STUPENDOUS MAN** LEAPS INTO THE CLOSET TO CHANGE BACK INTO HIS 6-YEAR-OLD ALTER EGO, MILD-MANNERED CALVIN!

CALVIN? ARE YOU IN HERE?

UNFORTUNATELY, **STUPENDOUS MAN'S** CAPE IS CAUGHT IN MILD-MANNERED CALVIN'S ZIPPER! CURSES!

THIS IS GOING TO BE A GOOD ONE, I CAN TELL.

GEEZ, MOM! CAN'T A GUY HAVE A LITTLE PRIVACY?!

AND WHY, MAY I ASK, ARE YOU STANDING IN YOUR UNDERWEAR IN THE CLOSET?

OH, NO REASON. UM... I WAS HOT.

YOU'RE **SUPPOSED** TO BE DOING YOUR HOMEWORK!

I DON'T NEED TO DO IT NOW, THANKS TO **STUPENDOUS MAN!**

OH YEAH?

IT WAS GREAT! HE FRIED THE SCHOOL WITH A BIG MAGNIFYING LENS IN SPACE! I'M SURE IT WILL BE IN ALL THE PAPERS TOMORROW.

BOY, SHE'LL BE IN TROUBLE WHEN SHE GIVES ME MY COSTUME BACK. **BIG** TROUBLE.

OCTOBER 12, 13, 14, 1989

Calvin and Hobbes by WATTERSON

I'M HO-OME!

HI, CALVIN. WHATCHA DOIN'?

OOF, GET THIS BIG LUMMOX OFF ME.

LOOK AT YOU! YOU DIDN'T EVEN CHANGE OUT OF YOUR SCHOOL CLOTHES!

HOW COULD I?! I DIDN'T EVEN GET IN THE DOOR!

EVERY DAY THIS MANIAC IS SO GLAD TO SEE ME THAT HE BLASTS OUT LIKE A BIG ORANGE TORPEDO! A *DOG* WILL JUST WAG ITS TAIL, BUT OF COURSE A *TIGER* HAS TO *POUNCE* ON YOU! STUPID ANIMAL!

HE POUNCES ON YOU?

OH, AND DON'T THINK HE DOESN'T ENJOY THE CUNNING AND TREACHERY OF IT ALL! TIGERS *LIVE* FOR THE THRILL OF A SNEAK ATTACK! IT'S THEIR EVIL NATURE!

HE'S JUST SITTING THERE.

OH, SURE, *BIG* DISGUISE! LIKE NO ONE CAN FATHOM THE SAVAGE MIND OF A JUNGLE CAT! *HA!* HE'S A KILLER TO THE CORE!

I WISH MY PARENTS WOULD MOVE. MY DIARY IS GETTING WEIRDER EVERY DAY.

YEAH, *YOU* KNOW WHO I'M TALKING ABOUT! WIPE OFF THAT GRIN OR *I'LL* DO IT *FOR* YOU!

October 15, 1989

Strip 1 (October 16)

Panel 1: UH OH, CALVIN THE REPTILE IS IN TROUBLE!

Panel 2: AS AN ECTOTHERM, HIS BODY RELIES ON THE ENVIRONMENT TO WARM OR COOL ITS TEMPERATURE.

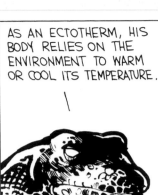

Panel 3: NOW THAT IT'S COLDER OUTSIDE, CALVIN'S BODY TEMPERATURE FALLS AND HE BECOMES SLUGGISH! HE'LL GO INTO TORPOR IF HE CAN'T FIND A WARM PLACE TO LIE!

Panel 4: LEAVE THE THERMOSTAT ALONE, AND PUT ON A SWEATER IF YOU'RE COLD.

I...I DON'T HAVE THE EN..ENERGY!

Strip 2 (October 17)

I HEARD THAT BIG CATS DON'T PURR.

THAT'S TRUE. WE'RE TOO FIERCE AND FEROCIOUS. WE DON'T EVER PURR.

WELL WHAT DO YOU CALL THE NOISE YOU MAKE WHEN YOU GET YOUR TUMMY RUBBED?!

GROWLING FRIENDLY-LIKE.

Strip 3 (October 18)

Panel 1: CALVIN, YOUR MOM AND I LOOKED OVER YOUR REPORT CARD, AND WE THINK YOU COULD BE DOING BETTER.

BUT I DON'T LIKE SCHOOL.

Panel 2: WHY NOT? YOU LIKE TO READ AND YOU LIKE TO LEARN. I KNOW YOU DO.

Panel 3: I MEAN, YOU'VE READ EVERY DINOSAUR BOOK EVER WRITTEN, AND YOU'VE LEARNED A LOT, RIGHT? READING AND LEARNING ARE FUN.

YEAH..

Panel 4: SO WHY DON'T YOU LIKE SCHOOL?

WE DON'T READ ABOUT DINOSAURS.

OCTOBER 16, 17, 18, 1989

October 19, 20, 21, 1989

October 22, 1989

OCTOBER 23, 24, 25, 1989

322

PAY ATTENTION TO ME.

I'VE GOT TO WRITE A REPORT FOR SCHOOL.

WHAT'S YOUR TOPIC?

BATS. CAN YOU IMAGINE ANYTHING MORE STUPID?

HECK, *I* DON'T KNOW ANYTHING ABOUT BATS.' HOW AM I SUPPOSED TO WRITE A REPORT ON A SUBJECT I KNOW NOTHING ABOUT?! IT'S IMPOSSIBLE!

I SUPPOSE RESEARCH IS OUT OF THE QUESTION.

OH, LIKE I'M GOING TO LEARN ABOUT BATS AND *THEN* WRITE A REPORT?! GIVE ME A BREAK!

HELLO, SUSIE? THIS IS CALVIN. YOU KNOW THIS REPORT WE'RE SUPPOSED TO WRITE FOR SCHOOL? YEAH. MY TOPIC IS BATS. WHAT'S YOURS?

ELEPHANTS? HMM. WELL, ARE YOU GOING TO THE LIBRARY TO LOOK UP ELEPHANTS? YOU ARE? GREAT!

WHILE YOU'RE THERE, COULD YOU RESEARCH BATS TOO, AND MAKE COPIES OF ALL THE INFORMATION YOU FIND, AND MAYBE UNDERLINE THE IMPORTANT PARTS FOR ME, AND SORT OF OUTLINE IT, SO I WOULDN'T HAVE TO READ IT ALL?

HOW'D IT GO?

I REALLY LOATHE GIRLS.

October 26, 27, 28, 1989

October 30, 31, November 1, 1989

ALL RIGHT, CLASS, WHO WOULD LIKE TO GIVE HIS REPORT FIRST?

I WOULD! I WOULD!

WHY CALVIN, WHAT A SURPRISE TO SEE YOU VOLUNTEER! YOU MUST HAVE DONE A GOOD JOB. GO TO THE FRONT OF THE CLASS.

OH BOY!

NOW LET'S ALL PAY ATTENTION. GO AHEAD, CALVIN.

THANK YOU. BEFORE I BEGIN, I'D LIKE EVERYONE TO NOTICE THAT MY REPORT IS IN A PROFESSIONAL, CLEAR PLASTIC BINDER.

THAT'S VERY NICE. GO AHEAD.

WHEN A REPORT LOOKS THIS GOOD, YOU KNOW IT'LL GET AN "A." THAT'S A TIP, KIDS, WRITE IT DOWN.

MY REPORT IS ON BATS. ...AHEM...

"DUSK! WITH A CREEPY, TINGLING SENSATION, YOU HEAR THE FLUTTERING OF LEATHERY WINGS! BATS! WITH GLOWING RED EYES AND GLISTENING FANGS, THESE UNSPEAKABLE GIANT BUGS DROP ONTO..."

BATS AREN'T BUGS!!

LOOK, WHO'S GIVING THE REPORT? YOU CHOWDERHEADS ...OR ME?!

CALVIN, I'D LIKE TO SEE YOU A MOMENT.

MAN ALIVE! CAN YOU BELIEVE WHAT MY TEACHER WROTE ON MY REPORT?

SHE SAYS I OBVIOUSLY DID NO RESEARCH WHATSOEVER ON BATS AND THAT MY SCIENTIFIC ILLUSTRATION LOOKS LIKE I TRACED THE BATMAN LOGO AND ADDED FANGS!

SHE'S PRETTY PERCEPTIVE.

SHE DIDN'T EVEN GIVE ME CREDIT FOR MY PROFESSIONAL CLEAR PLASTIC BINDER!

WHAT DID YOUR PARENTS HAVE TO SAY?

NOTHING. AND IF YOU'LL GIVE ME A HAND HERE, IT WILL STAY THAT WAY.

Calvin and Hobbes
by WATTERSON

WOW, HONEY, YOU'RE MISSING A BEAUTIFUL SUNSET OUT HERE!

I'LL COUNT TO 10, AND THEN... *POW!*

DAD, HOW COME OLD PHOTOGRAPHS ARE ALWAYS BLACK AND WHITE? DIDN'T THEY HAVE COLOR FILM BACK THEN?

SURE THEY DID. IN FACT, THOSE OLD PHOTOGRAPHS *ARE* IN COLOR. IT'S JUST THE *WORLD* WAS BLACK AND WHITE THEN.

REALLY?

YEP. THE WORLD DIDN'T TURN COLOR UNTIL SOMETIME IN THE 1930s, AND IT WAS PRETTY GRAINY COLOR FOR A WHILE, TOO.

THAT'S REALLY WEIRD.

WELL, TRUTH IS STRANGER THAN FICTION.

'BUT THEN WHY ARE OLD *PAINTINGS* IN COLOR?' IF THE WORLD WAS BLACK AND WHITE, WOULDN'T ARTISTS HAVE PAINTED IT THAT WAY?

NOT NECESSARILY. A LOT OF GREAT ARTISTS WERE INSANE.

BUT...BUT HOW COULD THEY HAVE PAINTED IN COLOR ANYWAY? WOULDN'T THEIR PAINTS HAVE BEEN SHADES OF GRAY BACK THEN?

OF COURSE, BUT THEY TURNED COLORS LIKE EVERYTHING ELSE DID IN THE '30s.

SO WHY DIDN'T OLD BLACK AND WHITE PHOTOS TURN COLOR TOO?

BECAUSE THEY WERE COLOR PICTURES OF BLACK AND WHITE, REMEMBER?

THE WORLD IS A COMPLICATED PLACE, HOBBES.

WHENEVER IT SEEMS THAT WAY, I TAKE A NAP IN A TREE AND WAIT FOR DINNER.

OCTOBER 29, 1989

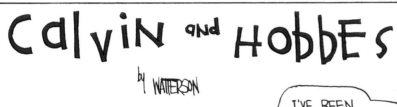

November 9, 10, 11, 1989

CalVin and HobbEs

by WATERSON

CRIICKK

I SURE WISH IT WOULD SNOW.

WHAT'S WITH THE SLED? THERE'S NO SNOW.

I AIM TO FIX *THAT* RIGHT NOW WITH AN APPEAL TO THE SNOW DEMONS.

SNOW DEMONS?

OBVIOUSLY THEY'RE TORMENTING US WITH THIS WIMPY WEATHER BECAUSE THEY'RE ANGRY. WE MUST APPEASE THEM.

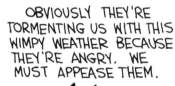

OH.

I'M GOING TO LIE HERE ON MY SLED AND THINK SNOW THOUGHTS UNTIL THE SNOW DEMONS HAVE MERCY AND UNLEASH A BLIZZARD.

SNOW, SNOW! HIGH AND LOW! WHEREVER WE GO! LET IT BLOW! TO AND FRO! HI-DE-HO! SNOW! SNOW! SNOW!

WELL, I'LL COME OUT IN EARLY JANUARY AND SEE HOW YOU'RE DOING.

TELL MOM I'LL NEED MY MEALS OUT HERE AND I WON'T BE GOING TO SCHOOL TOMORROW.

NOVEMBER 12, 1989

November 13, 14, 15, 1989

MOM AND DAD WON'T BE TOO HAPPY ABOUT *THIS*. NO SIR.

DAD WILL HAVE TO BOLT MY BED TO THE CEILING TONIGHT, AND MOM WILL HAVE TO STAND ON A STEPLADDER TO HAND ME DINNER.

THEN I'LL HAVE TO HOLD MY PLATE UPSIDE-DOWN ABOVE MY HEAD AND SCRAPE THE FOOD OFF THE UNDERSIDE! AND IF I SPILL ANYTHING, IT WILL FLY 10 FEET UP TO THE FLOOR AND SPLOT!

THIS IS GOING TO BE THE MOST FUN I'VE EVER HAD!

ALL THIS WIDE OPEN CEILING SPACE! I WISH I COULD GET MY ROLLER SKATES.

HEY, MAYBE I CAN CLIMB UP THIS BOOKCASE AND WHEN I GET TO THE BOTTOM SHELF, LEAP TO A CHAIR!

THEN I CAN PULL MYSELF ACROSS TO OTHER PIECES OF FURNITURE AND WORK MY WAY TO MY TOY CHEST.

...I CAN HEAR MOM NOW: "HOW ON EARTH DID YOU GET SNEAKER PRINTS ON THE UNDERSIDE OF EACH SHELF?!"

THERE! I THINK I CAN JUMP TO THAT CHAIR AND HANG ONTO THE BACK.

GEERONIMOOO!

¡WHOAAA!

WHAM!

GREAT. JUST GREAT.

CALVIN, QUIT BANGING AROUND!

November 16, 17, 18, 1989

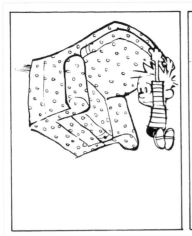

November 20, 21, 22, 1989

November 23, 24, 25, 1989

WELL? HOW'S YOUR MATH COMING ALONG?

I'VE ALMOST STARTED!

OH BROTHER! ANOTHER "DISCUSSION" ABOUT MY STUDY HABITS AND THE IMPORTANCE OF HOMEWORK.

I TRIED EXPLAINING THAT IT'S HARD TO STUDY WHEN ONE'S SIZE SUDDENLY STARTS INCREASING, BUT DOES *SHE* CARE?! HAH!

NO, IT'S JUST BLAH BLAH BLAH, LIKE IT'S ALL *MY* FAULT! MOM'S NEVER BEEN AS BIG AS A GALAXY, SO SHE CAN'T UNDERSTAND HOW ANYONE *ELSE* COULD BE! SHEEESH.

OOPS, IT LOOKS LIKE SHE'S WRAPPING UP. BETTER START NODDING.

GOOD. I'M GLAD WE HAD THIS LITTLE TALK.

DOING HOMEWORK?

YEAHHHH... BOY, YOU MISSED THE SHOW.

I GOT A BIG LECTURE FROM MOM JUST BECAUSE I GOT STUCK ON THE CEILING AND THEN GREW SO BIG I FELL OFF THE PLANET WHEN I WAS SUPPOSED TO BE DOING MY MATH!

GEE, *THAT'S* NOT VERY FAIR.

YOU SAID IT. HERE, HOW ABOUT HELPING ME HURRY UP WITH THESE PROBLEMS?

SURE! TIGERS ARE GREAT AT MATH! NOW WHAT DO THESE LITTLE HORIZONTAL LINES MEAN?

THAT'S A MINUS SIGN. LET ME KNOW WHEN YOU'RE DONE, OK? I'LL BE READING COMIC BOOKS.

NOVEMBER 30, DECEMBER 1, 2, 1989

November 19, 1989

November 26, 1989

December 3, 1989

December 4, 5, 6, 1989

December 7, 8, 9, 1989

Calvin and Hobbes
by Watterson

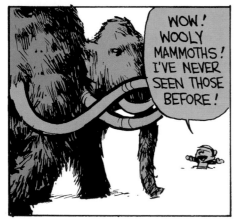

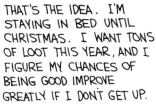

December 11, 12, 13, 1989

CALVIN and HOBBES

by WATTERSON

'TIS THE SEASON TO ADVERTISE.

CALVIN, LOOK! YOU GOT A LETTER!

A LETTER? I DIDN'T HEAR THE MAIL TRUCK. A LETTER FOR ME?

THE RETURN ADDRESS SAYS "NORTH POLE".

OH MY GOSH, IT MUST BE FROM *SANTA*! SANTA SENT ME A LETTER! WOW! GEE!

READ IT! READ IT!

"DEAR CALVIN, YOU ROTTEN LITTLE KID..."

OH NO!! SANTA CALLED ME *ROTTEN*! I'M DOOMED!

KEEP READING.

"I MADE A LIST, BUT I DIDN'T BOTHER CHECKING IT TWICE, BECAUSE OBVIOUSLY YOU'RE THE NAUGHTIEST KID IN THE WHOLE WORLD."

AUGH!

WHAT ELSE?

"I'M WRITING TO GIVE YOU ONE LAST CHANCE. YOU'VE GOT SEVEN DAYS TO GET ON THE 'GOOD BOY' LIST."

SEVEN DAYS!! OH NO! WHAT CAN I *DO??*

MAYBE HE SAYS.

"I'D SUGGEST YOU START BY BEING KIND TO ANIMALS. PERHAPS YOU KNOW AN ANIMAL WHO WOULD LIKE A SNACK SOON. OR MAYBE YOU SHOULD LET AN ANIMAL READ YOUR COMIC BOOKS SOMETIME. THINK ABOUT IT."

SOUNDS LIKE SAGE ADVICE.

"SIGNED, SANTA CLAWS." *SANTA CLAWS?* WAIT A MINUTE! *I* RECOGNIZE THIS HANDWRITING! IT'S *YOURS*! SANTA DIDN'T WRITE THIS AT ALL!!

GIVE YOU A SNACK, HUH?! HOW ABOUT A KNUCKLE SANDWICH?!

HMPH. WELL, IT'S WHAT SANTA *WOULD'VE* WRITTEN IF HE WASN'T SO BUSY NOW.

DECEMBER 17, 1989

December 18, 19, 20, 1989

December 21, 22, 23, 1989

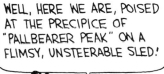

December 25, 26, 27, 1989

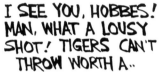

December 28, 29, 30, 1989

December 31, 1989